POSITION
OF THE
WEEK

ICE HOUSE BOOKS

Published by Ice House Books

Copyright © 2021 Lovehoney Group Ltd. Lovehoney® is a
registered trademark of Lovehoney Group Ltd, Bath, BA1 3EN

Ice House Books is an imprint of Half Moon Bay Limited
Stephens Way, Warminster, BA12 8PE
www.icehousebooks.co.uk

The material in this publication is of the nature of general
comment only, and does not represent professional advice.

ISBN 978-1-913308-19-3

Printed in China

TO

FROM

WELCOME

This little book contains 52 sexual positions – one for every week of the year.

The positions range from very simple to a little more challenging and can easily be adapted, meaning there's something for everyone.

Share the book with your partner and have some fun experimenting!

CONSENT

Have a conversation
with your partner before
trying new positions,
to ensure everyone
involved is having fun.

If something is painful
or uncomfortable,
stop immediately.

Everything you do
together should be
100% consensual.

1

ON YOUR MARKS

The bottom squats on their tiptoes with their knees bent and palms on the floor to help support and balance their body. The top kneels behind them and straightens their body in an upright position, with their hands on their partner's buttocks. While the top penetrates them, the bottom can use their partner's thighs to bounce up and down.

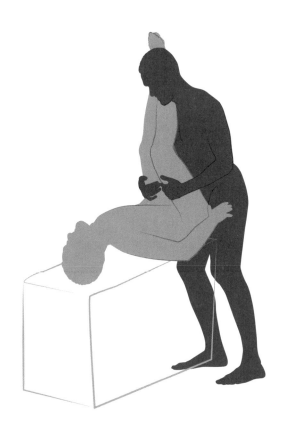

2

SOFA SURFER

The bottom sits on the armrest of a sofa and carefully lowers their upper body down onto the seat, with their legs straight and raised. The top stands in front of the bottom and places the bottom's legs on their shoulders while wrapping their arms around their thighs. Add a cock ring (or two) to catapult this position to the next level.

AEROPLANE

The top sits on the floor with their legs spread apart. The bottom sits on the top's lap with their back to them and their legs straight and spread wide apart. This is a fantastic position for penetration and frees up both partners' hands for mutual masturbation.

DOUBLE DUTY

One partner kneels and bends forward, lifting their butt in the air and resting the top half of their body on the floor. The other partner kneels behind them and manoeuvres their lover's hips and butt cheeks to give them oral pleasure. This position is great for rimming, and both partners can use their hands to stimulate their own penis and testicles.

MIRROR MIRROR

One partner goes on all fours in a slightly raised position, with their knees apart. The other partner lies on their back with their head between their partner's legs and their own legs bent at the knees and hip-width apart. The person lying down can grab hold of their partner's buttocks to help guide them, while the other partner can lean back or move forward. This position allows both partners to pleasure each other simultaneously with their mouth and hands.

A LEG UP

The bottom gets on all fours, with their legs apart and feet together. They then extend forward in a stretching cat-like pose, with their arms in front of them and bent at the elbows. The top kneels on one knee between the bottom's legs, and places the other knee over their butt. One hand is placed on the bottom's butt, and the other on their back.

7

WILD THING

The top rises up on their knees and leans back slightly. The bottom straddles them, wrapping their legs around their waist and their arms around their shoulders. The top can pull their partner in tight by hugging them around their waist. The closeness of your bodies and direct eye contact add to the intensity of the experience.

MIGHTY KNEEL

The top lies on their back with their head resting on a pillow and their legs wide apart. The bottom kneels between their partner's legs, facing away from them with their legs positioned either side of their thighs. The bottom's hands should be placed on the floor in between their legs, while the top places their hands on their partner's butt or hips.

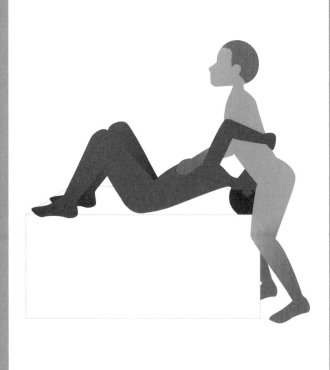

RISE AND SHINE

One partner lies on their back on a bed, with their head hanging off the edge. Their legs should be bent at the knees and apart. The other partner stands on the floor facing them and stretches their arms out front, resting their hands on their partner's torso. The horizontal partner performs oral sex on the standing partner, holding on to their thighs or torso to pull them in closer. Add your favourite flavoured lube into the mix for extra-delicious licks and sucks.

TINGLE ALL THE WAY

The top sits on the bed or floor with their hands behind them for balance and support. Their legs should be slightly bent at the knees and crossed at the ankles to form a triangle shape. The bottom sits on their partner's lap, facing them. They lean back with their arms stretched out behind them, and their legs bent with their feet resting on the shoulders of their partner.

HEAVENLY RAISE

The bottom lies on their back with their legs in the air, while the top faces them and leans into their legs. The top can control the pace of thrusting, and use the bottom's raised legs for support. The bottom can accessorise their free-roaming hands with a stroker. If you'd like to share a little extra buzz, the top could wear a vibrating cock ring to ramp things up in the pleasure stakes.

THE DEEP DIVE

The bottom lies with their back on the floor and lifts their butt and legs in the air, until they are supporting their body with just their shoulders (they can use their arms to help prop them up for extra support). The top should then straddle them in a squat-like position, facing away from them and holding on to their buttocks for extra balance and help with each thrust.

ON YOUR KNEES

Both partners kneel and face each other in an intimate embrace, with their thighs touching and arms pulling their torsos in close together. This position creates all of the excitement and build-up of foreplay, but in an incredibly intimate scenario. Go to town on toys in this position, whether you choose strokers or butt plugs, and maintain eye contact throughout to intensify every touch and caress.

14

HOLD ON TIGHT

Stand facing each other. The bottom wraps their legs around the top's body (with a little helping hand). The top holds on to their partner's thighs for support, while the bottom wraps their arms around the top's shoulders. Take full advantage of a wall for added stability, so the top can thrust harder and faster, and the bottom can enjoy deliciously deep penetration and P-spot stimulation.

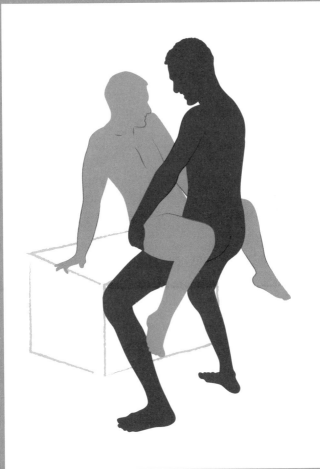

HOT SQUAT

The bottom sits in a chair, holding on to its edges with their hands. They then recline back slightly and spread their legs apart. The top stands or squats between the bottom's thighs, with their hands supporting their partner's buttocks.

16

STAND TO ATTENTION

Aim for the P-spot to hit the bullseye of intimate pleasure. The bottom kneels on the edge of a low bed or sofa. The top kneels behind them with their hands positioned around the bottom's waist to help pull them in close for penetration. Both partners' hands are free, so why not add tingly vibrations to the mix with a finger vibrator?

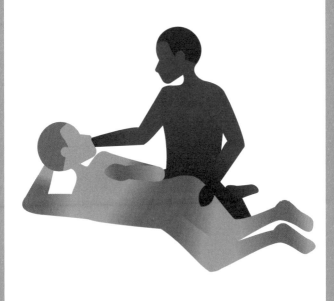

THE GOOD SIDE

The bottom lies sideways, holding their head with one arm bent at the elbow and their knees slightly bent. The top kneels behind them, with their knees wide apart to aid penetration. Try adding in a vibrator to boost your shared pleasure levels in an instant.

18

CHAIRWAY TO HEAVEN

It's not often that you hear the words 'press-up' and 'incredible pleasure' used together but trust us, this version of the exercise is sure to satisfy. The bottom gets into a press-up position over a sturdy chair, with their torso supported by the seat and their hands and toes on the floor. The top positions their body above their partner, with their torso raised and their hands placed on the seat of the chair.

BEST SEAT IN THE HOUSE

In this position, the bottom's internal pleasure spots will be showered with attention, while both partners' hands are free to explore external erogenous zones. The top sits in a chair and leans their body back, keeping their knees together with their feet lifted and toes on the floor. The bottom straddles the seated partner, facing away from them, with their body leaning slightly forward.

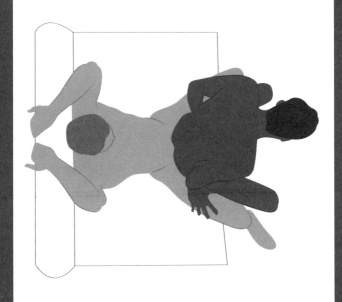

REVERSE COWBOY

Lean back and let your lover ride you. Sit or lie in a comfortable position while your partner, facing away from you, controls the depth and speed of penetration. You can wear a vibrating cock ring to add vibrations that you can both enjoy, or they can wear one to add even more pleasure to their experience – for maximum oomph, you could both wear one.

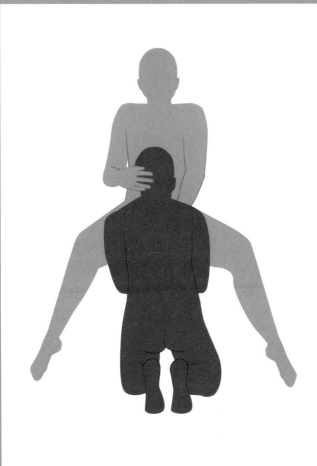

21

TAKE A SEAT

One partner sits on a chair with their thighs apart. The other partner kneels in between their feet and treats the seated partner to an incredible oral session. This position is fantastic for couples looking to explore dominant and submissive roles, as it puts the receiving partner in the driving seat.

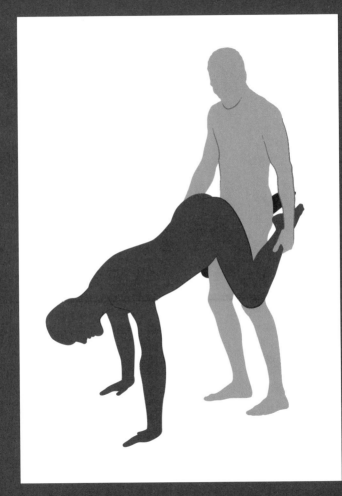

THE WHEELBARROW

The top starts with their back against a wall. The bottom then places their hands on the ground, while the top holds on to their partner's calves to support them. If you want to add an extra buzz, why not add a vibrating cock ring (or two) into the mix?

ROCK STAR

With strain and pressure on the legs taken away, you can both rock and grind away with complete ease and comfort. The bottom kneels on their partner with their feet either side of them, using the top's legs for balance and support. The top keeps their feet on the floor and holds on to the bottom's waist.

24

MISSIONARY

It may not top the list for innovation, but there's no denying that missionary can be mind-blowing. You're face to face, which means up close and personal, thrilling and intimate. Penetration isn't necessarily required, either: you can also explore frotting (penis-to-penis contact) in the missionary position.

25

BUMPER CARS

Up for a challenge? In this position, the top has gravity on their side while they penetrate the bottom. For added stimulation, the top could slip on a penis extender to enhance their length or girth, or wear a textured penis sleeve for added thrills. Facing in opposite directions, you can both thrust and grind away to your hearts' content.

26

SPOONING

Not only is it great for cuddling, spooning can make for slow-but-sensational sex, too. This versatile position is highly enjoyable both with and without penetration, and adding a bullet vibe to the mix can heighten the excitement even more. Curl around your partner and grind your hips together. If you're not penetrating them, try sliding your penis between their legs or ass cheeks for a different thrill.

27

RIDING GRIND/ POLE STROKE

In one corner: Riding Grind, a position that combines the intimacy of missionary with the depth of doggy style. In the other corner: Pole Stroke, a non-penetrative position where partners rub their penises together while face to face. Well, don't feel obligated to choose – start out stroking poles before moving into a more energetic, riding grind. Face one another, with one partner straddling the other's lap. This gives great access for deep penetration or frotting. Wearing a cock ring may help boost your staying power if you're planning on making a night of it.

28

DOGGY STYLE

A classic for a reason, doggy style allows for deep, controlled penetration. The bottom gets on all fours – or another comfortable position with their butt in the air – and the top penetrates them from behind. If you've ever fantasised about adding a third person to the mix, why not mimic that feeling by adding in a stroker as well?

69

Bring things right to *ahem* a head with oral for both of you! This is a great way to give what you get: try matching them motion for motion for totally synchronised sensations. Splash on your fave flavoured lubricant, then lie on your side opposite your partner and pleasure them orally.

RIMMING

The entrance to the anus is full of sensitive nerve-endings that can feel amazing when licked. Alternate between a flat, wide tongue for gentle strokes, and a stiff, pointed tip for precision. Try mixing up your tongue movements, and applying different pressures and speeds to see what your partner prefers. A drizzle of flavoured lube can make things even more pleasurable.

31

BUTT AND GRIND

If you like to see the results of your handiwork, this is the position for you. Whether you're penetrating your partner or rubbing against them, you've got a great view of your penis while you play. The bottom lies flat on their stomach and the top kneels behind them, sliding their penis between their partner's ass cheeks without penetrating them (at least to begin with). Add a butt plug or prostate massager to increase excitement for the top.

32

MUTUAL MASTURBATION

Chances are you've got some special solo moves you use to drive yourself over the edge. Well, sharing is caring. In this position, you can use your favourite stroker or penis-teasing techniques on each other for a super shared session. Settle into a comfortable position side by side and tease each other with your hands or toys.

SKY HIGH

The bottom warms up in the reverse cowboy position (straddling the top while facing away from them) before leaning back and pulling their legs out in front of them. With the bottom's legs raised and held up with their hands, the top will need to support their partner by wrapping their hands around their torso. The top can help achieve balance and extra thrusting power by placing their feet on the ground with their knees far apart.

34

THE HAMMOCK

Feel like you're flying without joining the Mile High Club! This position is a bit of a challenge, so make sure the top is sitting on something sturdy before you begin. Facing in the same direction as their partner, the bottom sits on the top's lap to be penetrated. The top leans back and the bottom leans forward until lying almost straight. The top holds on to their partner's wrists, and the bottom digs their heels into the top's back for balance.

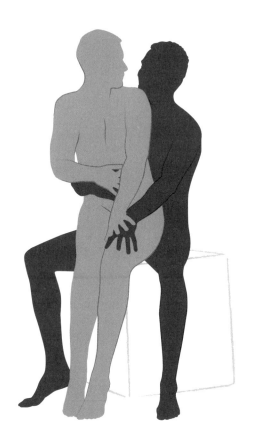

35

THE THRONE

The top sits on a chair or bed with their legs wide apart, and the bottom moves back onto their partner's penis. The top can use a lubed-up stroker on their partner's penis, matching the rhythm of each thrust for a perfectly synchronised pleasure session.

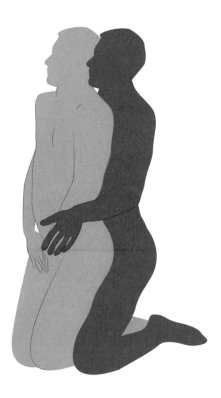

36

THE GRIND

Start in the traditional doggy-style pose with the bottom on all fours and the top behind. The top supports their partner with their hands while the bottom rises up on their knees. It's super easy for the top to reach around and stimulate the bottom's penis in this position. For even more pleasure, add a vibrating stroker into the mix.

HORSE AND CARRIAGE

The bottom lies on their back with their legs pulled up towards their head. The top gets into a press-up position, facing away from their partner and straddling them with their knees to maximise stability and control. The top could wear a butt plug for deliciously heightened sensations.

38

PARK AND RIDE

This is a great way to switch up your usual roles. The top lies on their back with their legs bent and feet raised off the floor, pointing towards the ceiling. The bottom faces away on all fours and shifts back towards their partner's penis. The top can take hold of the bottom's ankles to help them achieve the perfect position.

39

GRIP IT GOOD

The bottom lies on their back with their legs spread out (similar to missionary) and their head supported by a pillow or something firm and soft. The top kneels in front and holds their partner's waist to raise their thighs and bring their pelvis closer. The bottom wraps their legs around the top's waist and locks them tightly behind their partner's back. The top could try wearing a vibrating butt plug or cock ring for an extra buzz.

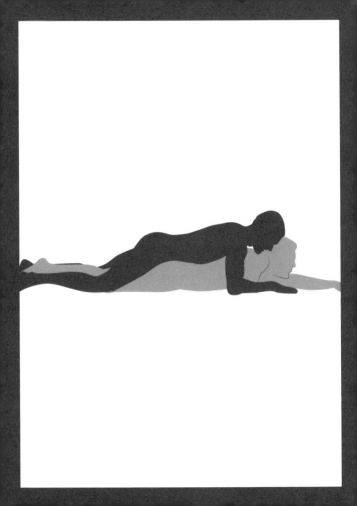

THE SANDWICH

The bottom lies flat on their front and keeps their legs closed. The top lies on their partner, with their legs either side of them. Add another sexy dimension to this position by introducing vibrating toys and position enhancers for even more pleasure.

CHEEK TO CHEEK

One partner gets into a horizontal, face-down position, with their hips resting on a sturdy cushion or padded footrest and their arms on the floor. The other partner kneels behind and gently prizes their lover's thighs and butt cheeks apart, to give them a rimming session they won't forget in a hurry.

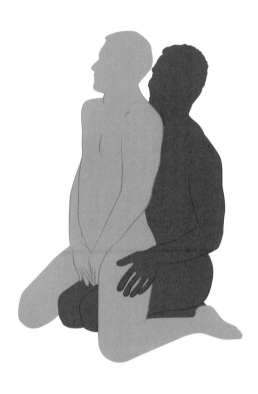

42

BACK IN THE SADDLE

This is a very intimate position that encourages physical communication and frees up both partners' hands for extra stimulation during penetration. The top kneels with their knees together. The bottom straddles their partner with their back to them, placing their knees either side of the top's legs and edging onto them in a seated position.

DEEP DIVING

Get into position and prepare for a whole lotta pleasure from your Deep Diving expedition. The bottom kneels on all fours, while the top kneels behind with one knee raised. The top picks up their partner's leg and rests it on their raised knee, tilting the bottom's hips into a right angle and supporting their raised leg and body with their hands. The top can then manoeuvre into the best position for penetration.

LAID-BACK LOVERS

The top lies down. The bottom squats over them then carefully leans back, with their feet on the ground to help them gain control over their movements. It's even better if you add a buzzing cock ring or two to the mix.

THE KITE

The bottom lies on their back with their feet together and knees opened out to the sides. The top kneels and holds their partner's feet for maximum control over each thrust. Try adding a vibrating stroker into the mix for an even more explosive session.

THE CLOSE-UP

The Close-Up allows you to get up close, very personal and in a prime position to please. Go slow or turn it into a fast and explosive sex session – you decide. The bottom lies on their side with their top leg raised slightly. The top lies next to them on their side, and cradles them close before penetrating from behind. The top holds the bottom's thigh and raises it higher to aid extra-deep penetration.

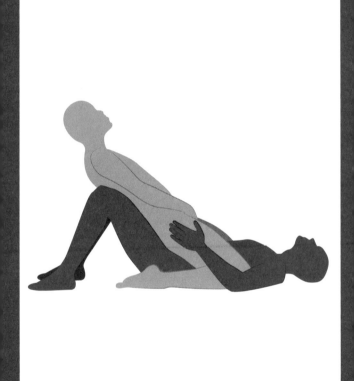

48

PLEASURE SLIDE

The top lies on their back with their feet on the floor and knees raised. The bottom straddles the top's knees, leaning on their partner's thighs and using them to support their upper body. Intensify sensations by adding a remote control prostate massager for the top, with their partner in charge of the pleasure settings for a stimulation showdown.

49

LIFT-OFF

This position will get your blood pumping for all the right reasons. The bottom lies on their front and the top approaches from behind in a kneeling position. The bottom shifts back onto their partner with their torso raised and both hands on the floor, and places their legs either side of the top's thighs in a stretched-out position. The top moves their hands to their partner's hips for gentle support and to aid penetration. The fact that both partners are facing away from each other should enhance every touch.

50

DINNER DATE

One partner lies on their back and raises both legs, using their hands to support their lower back. The other partner kneels with their knees facing their partner's shoulders, and leans forward so that their face is between their partner's legs. Why not add to the pleasure platter with a drizzle of flavoured lube?

OVER THE RAINBOW

The bottom lies on their back with their knees bent and pressed to their chest. The top lies across the bottom in a press-up position, using their arms and knees to support their weight and aid each thrust. The beauty of this position is that you can tailor the depth and angle of penetration in an instant to discover what makes for a sensational session.

52

THE WATERFALL

The top sits with their arms back and legs wide, while the bottom lies in front, lifts their ankles onto their partner's shoulders, then lifts their butt so the top can penetrate them. Try a position enhancer for easier and more comfortable penetration, and why not add a stroker into the mix for the bottom?

Liked this book?
Try these out next!